My First
Steps to
Learning

My First Workbook

Written by
Liane B. Onish

📖 SCHOLASTIC

New York   Toronto   London   Auckland   Sydney
Mexico City   New Delhi   Hong Kong   Buenos Aires

Design by Witz End Design, LLC

Illustrations by Ben Mahan (all new art for this workbook, as well as the art from My One Book and My Seven Book), Colin King (art from all the Alphabet Books, A to Z), Rusty Fletcher (My Three Book, My Six Book), Kate Flanagan (My Two Book, My Six Book), Ellen Sasaki (My Four Book), Paige Keiser (My Eight Book), Anna DiVito (My Nine Book), and John Jones (My Ten Book).

ISBN 0-439-91182-6

Published by Scholastic Inc.

12 11 10 9 8 7 6 5 4 3 2 1   8 9 10 11 12/0

Printed in the U.S.A.

First Scholastic printing, January 2007

Table of Contents

Dear Parents

Teaching young children has been one of the great joys of my life. I cherish every opportunity to catch a sparkle of tomorrow in each child I meet. Our children are truly our treasures. That is why it is a privilege for me to invite you to join your child in this learning adventure with the **My First Steps to Learning** program.

You are also a teacher, your child's first teacher. You have been teaching the language of love and learning from the very beginning. As your child finds name-labels for the important things in his life, he is on his way to learning language. As your child shows an interest in reading words and counting, you'll know you have reached important milestones. This program is designed to help you capitalize on this natural curiosity.

In the **My First Steps to Learning Workbook**, you'll discover many helpful activities and games for your child to explore with you. The Workbook is divided into three major sections, each designed for specific learning goals.

- The first section, **Learning Letters**, explores letter names, sounds, and writing letters.
- **Learning Numbers** will help your child discover ways to count items in groups, and how to match and trace numerals and number words as well.
- The final section, **Learning First Words**, gives your child an opportunity to match words and pictures and write initial letters of pictures.

As you begin the Workbook, let your child's enthusiasm and attention span guide you. Encourage and support whatever piques your child's interest. While each of us follows a similar growth pattern, each is uniquely different. Your child may enjoy one page at a time. Another may like to do two pages. One child may love to color objects. Another will prefer to mark an object with a crayon. You will be surprised by how much fun you and your child will have as you take these steps together.

Sincerely,

Jane Belk Moncure

Using the Workbook

The workbook pages have special features that you won't want to miss!

Activity Boxes You'll find extra games and activities that are fun and easy to do in the Parent Activity Boxes. They also provide extra practice in letter recognition and other essential skills.

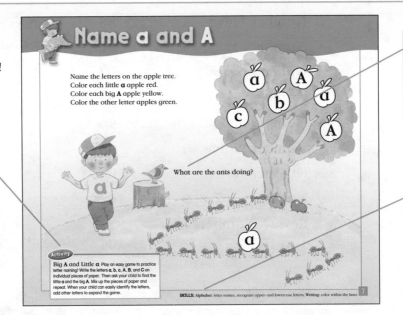

Oral Activity Each open-ended question is designed to encourage oral vocabulary development. Help your child exercise and expand his or her speaking vocabulary by providing words he or she may need to answer the oral activity questions.

Skills Footer The skills footer at the bottom of the page indicates the specific skills that are the focus of the page. The letter name is followed by slashes. Within the slash marks is the sound the letter stands for. For example: a/a/ is shorthand for: "the letter a/the first sound in the word ant/."

Learning Letters

Little **a**, Little **b**, Little **c**, and all the other letter kids want you to learn their names, hear their sounds, and write their letters! In this section, you'll find that the pages for each letter explore these concepts and skills:

- **Alphabet Recognition:** To learn to read, your child must be able to name the letters and identify their written forms.

- **Phonemic Awareness:** Words are made up of a series of separate individual sounds called **phonemes**. Before children can learn to read, they need to be able to hear the sounds that make up words.

- **Phonics:** Phonics teaches children the relationship between sounds and the symbols we use to represent them. This sound-spelling relationship is essential to reading and writing.

- **Writing:** All the workbook pages provide pre-writing and writing practice. Coloring outlined letters and pictures strengthen your child's control over fine-motor tasks.

Sing the ABC Song

Do you know the ABC song?
Sing the song and touch the letters as you sing them.
Then touch the letters in your name!

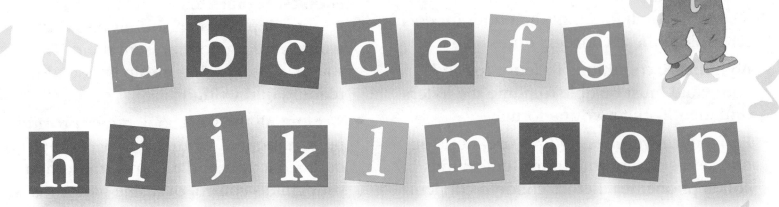

Now I know my abc's.
Next time won't you sing with me?

Name a and A

Name the letters on the apple tree.
Color each little **a** apple red.
Color each big **A** apple yellow.
Color the other letter apples green.

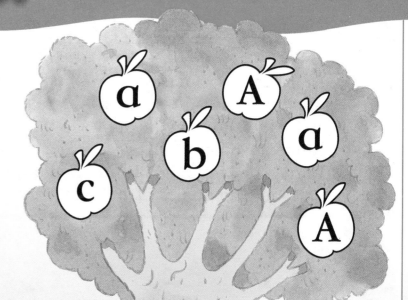

What are the ants doing?

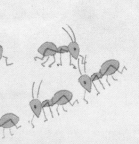

Activity

Big A and Little a Play an easy game to practice letter naming! Write the letters **a**, **b**, **c**, **A**, **B**, and **C** on individual pieces of paper. Then ask your child to find the little **a** and the big **A**. Mix up the pieces of paper and repeat. When your child can easily identify the letters, add other letters to expand the game.

SKILLS: Alphabet: letter names, recognize upper- and lowercase letters; **Writing:** color within the lines

Hear the Short a Sound

Help Little  put the **a** words in the sound box.
Apples begins with the short **a** sound.
Trace the line from the apples to the sound box.
Name the other pictures.
Draw a line from the pictures that begin with the
first sound in **apples** to the sound box.

a, A

Phonics Note
The letter **a** stands for two sounds: short
a as in **a**pple, and long **a** as in **a**corn.

8 **SKILLS: Phonemic Awareness:** short a/a/; **Writing:** draw lines right-to-left

Write a and A

Use your finger to trace the letters.
Start at the big dot.
Then use a crayon to trace and write the letters.

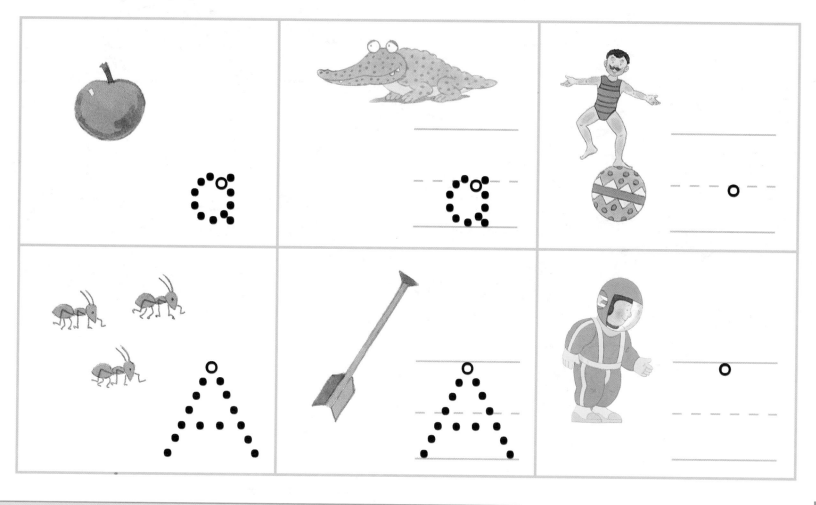

SKILLS: Writing: finger-trace and write letters a, A

Name b and B

Name the letters on the beach balls.
Draw blue dots on each little **b** ball.
Draw red stripes on each big **B** ball.
Color the other letter balls your favorite colors.

b   B   a   b   c   B

What are your favorite colors?

SKILLS: Alphabet: letter names, recognize upper- and lowercase letters; **Writing**: draw dots and stripes, color within the lines

Hear the b Sound

Little  wants to play with the **balls** that begin with the **b** sound.
Color the balls with pictures of things that begin like the word **ball**.
Then draw a line from each ball you colored to the basket.

b, B

SKILLS: Phonemic Awareness: b/b/; **Writing:** color within the lines, draw lines top-to-bottom

Write b and B

Use your finger to trace the letters on the balloons.
Start at the big dot.
Then use a crayon to trace and write the letters.

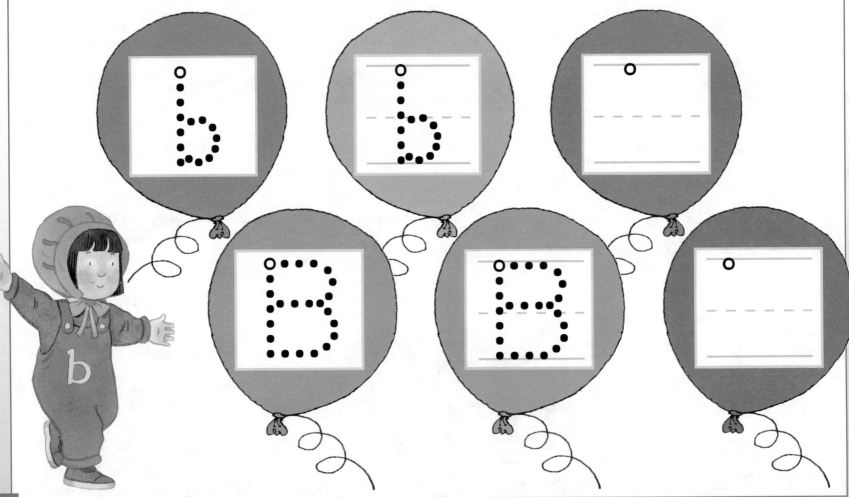

SKILLS: Writing: finger-trace and write letters b, B

Name c and C

Name the letters on the cups.
Color each little **c** cup blue.
Color each big **C** cup yellow.
Color the other letter cups red.

What do you drink out of a cup?

SKILLS: Alphabet: letter names, recognize upper- and lowercase letters; **Writing:** color within the lines

Little  has a new camera.
Camera begins with the hard **c** sound.
Help Little **c** take pictures of things that begin
with the first sound in **camera**.
Draw a box around the things she will snap.
Draw an X on the things that do **not** begin
with the same sound as **camera**.

Phonics Note
The letter **c** stands for two sounds:
hard **c** as in **c**at, and soft **c** as in **c**ircle.

SKILLS: Phonemic Awareness: hard c/k/; Writing: draw boxes and the letter X

Use your finger to trace the letters on the cookies.
Start at the big dot.
Then use a crayon to trace and write the letters.

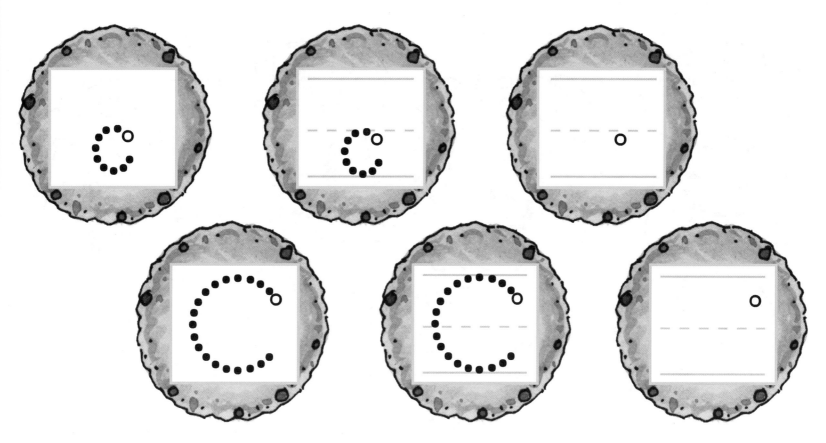

What other foods begins with the same sound as **cookie**?

SKILLS: Writing: finger-trace and write letters c, C; Phonemic Awareness: hard c/k/

Name d and D

Name the letters on the doll dresses.
Color each little **d** dress yellow.
Color each big **D** dress blue.
Color the other letter dresses green.

What dolls and stuffed animals do you have?

Activity

That's **D** One! Write the letters **a, A, c, C, d, d, d, D, D, D, f,** and **F** on one side of 12 index cards. Mix up the cards and put them in a pile facedown. Turn over the top card. If it's **d** or **D**, slap the card. If it's a different letter, call out the letter name.

SKILLS: Alphabet: letter names, recognize upper- and lowercase letters; **Writing:** color within the lines

Hear the d Sound

Help Little  put the **d** words in the doghouse.
Doll begins with the **d** sound.
Trace the line from the doll to the doghouse.
Name the other pictures.
Draw a line from the pictures that begin with the first sound in **doll** to the doghouse.

SKILLS: Phonemic Awareness: d/d/; Writing: draw lines

Write d and D

Use your finger to trace the letters by the dogs.
Start at the big dot.
Then use a crayon to trace and write the letters.

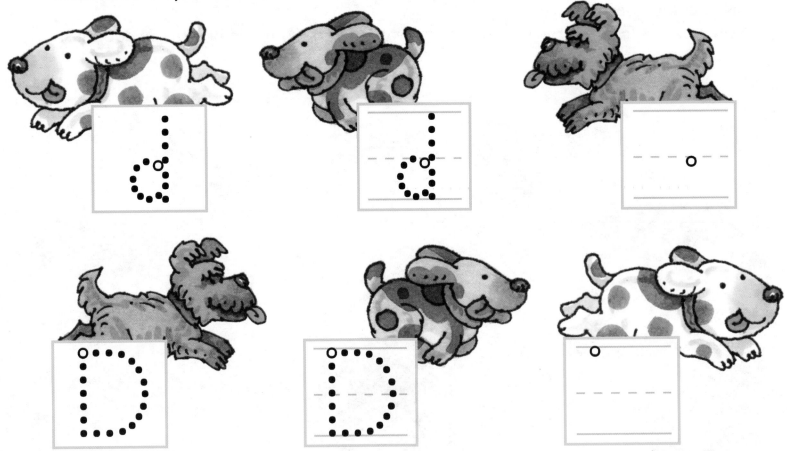

How are the dogs alike? How are they different?

SKILLS: Writing: finger-trace and write letters d, D

Name the letters on the eggs.
Color each little **e** egg blue.
Color each big **E** egg yellow.
Draw stripes on the other letter eggs.

e D E c

E e

How do you like to eat eggs?

Activity

Popular **e**, **E** Did you know that the letter **e** is the most popular letter in the English language? Share that fact with your child. Then on a piece of paper, write a family name that has one or more **e**'s in it. Have your child find and circle each **e**. Then go on an **e** hunt in your child's library, looking for this common letter in book titles.

SKILLS: Alphabet: letter names, recognize upper- and lowercase letters; **Writing:** color within the lines, draw stripes

Help Little  find the **e** pictures.
Elf begins with the short **e** sound.
Trace the line under the elf.
Name the other pictures.
Draw a line under the pictures that begin with the first sound in **elf**.

Phonics Note
The letter **e** has two sounds: short **e** as in **e**lf, and long **e** as in **e**agle.

SKILLS: Phonemic Awareness: short e/e/; **Writing:** learn to underline

Write e and E

Use your finger to trace the letters on the elephants.
Start at the big dot.
Then use a crayon to trace and write the letters.

SKILLS: Writing: finger-trace and write letters e, E

Name f and F

Name the letters on the fish.
Draw green dots on each little **f** fish.
Draw blue stripes on each big **F** fish.
Color the other letter fish any color you want.

Where do fish live?

SKILLS: Alphabet: letter names, recognize upper- and lowercase letters; **Writing:** draw dots and stripes, color within the lines

Hear the f Sound

Help Little 🧍 find **f** words in the forest.
Fan begins with the **f** sound.
Trace the circle around the fan.
Name the other things in the forest.
Draw a circle around the things that begin with the first sound in **fan**.
Draw an X on the things that do **not** begin like **fan**.

SKILLS: Phonemic Awareness: f/f/; Writing: draw circles and the letter X

Write f and F

Use your finger to trace the letters on the flags.
Start at the big dot.
Then use a crayon to trace and write the letters.

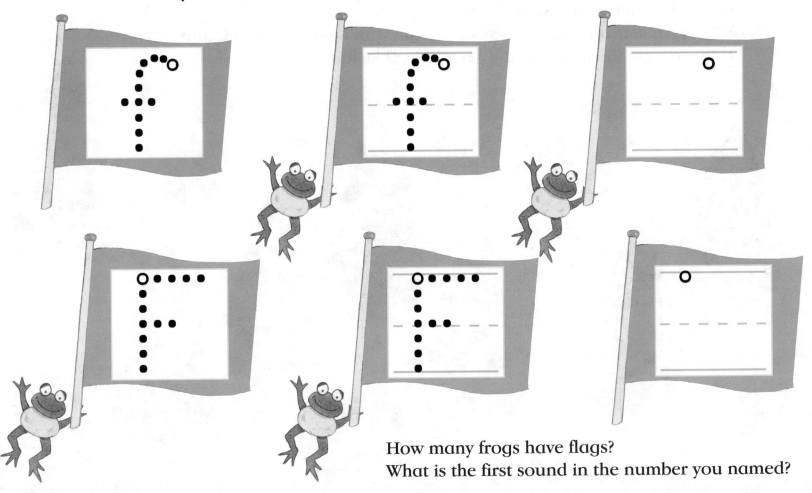

How many frogs have flags?
What is the first sound in the number you named?

SKILLS: Writing: finger-trace and write letters f, F

Name g and G

Name the letters on the bunches of grapes.
Color each little **g** grape bunch green.
Color each big **G** grape bunch red.
Color the other letter grapes blue.

Activity

Alphabet Shopping Turn your next grocery shopping trip into a fun game by having an alphabet hunt. As you walk through the supermarket aisles, call out a letter of the alphabet for your child to find. Each time your child finds a letter on a sign or package, ask him to tell you if it's a "big" or "little" letter.

What is your favorite fruit?

SKILLS: Alphabet: letter names, recognize upper- and lowercase letters; **Writing:** color within the lines

Help Little put the **g** words in the sound box.
Guitar begins with the hard **g** sound.
Trace the line from the guitar to the sound box.
Name the other pictures.
Draw a line from the pictures that begin with the first sound in **guitar** to the box.

g, G

Phonics Note
The letter **g** stands for two sounds: hard **g** as in **g**oat, and soft **g** as in **g**iraffe.

SKILLS: Phonemic Awareness: hard g/g/; Writing: draw diagonal lines

Write g and G

Use your finger to trace the letters by the geese.
Start at the big dot.
Then use a crayon to trace and write the letters.

SKILLS: Writing: finger-trace and write letters g, G

Name the letters on the hats.
Draw red dots on each little **h** hat.
Draw green stripes on each big **H** hat.
Color the other letter hats yellow.

What does your favorite hat look like?

SKILLS: Alphabet: letter names, recognize upper- and lowercase letters; **Writing:** draw dots and stripes, color within the lines

Hear the h Sound

Little **h** wants to put all the things that begin with the **h** sound in his helicopter.
Hat begins with the **h** sound.
Trace the circle around the hat and then draw a line from it to the helicopter.
Name the other pictures.
Circle each picture that begins with the same sound as **hat**.
Then draw a line from each thing you circled to the helicopter.

SKILLS: Phonemic Awareness: h/h/; Writing: draw circles, draw lines right-to-left

Write h and H

Use your finger to trace the letters on the house.
Start at the big dot.
Then use a crayon to trace and write the letters.

What does your house look like?

SKILLS: Writing: finger-trace and write letters h, H

Name the letters the inchworms are making.
Color each little **i** inchworm green.
Color each big **I** inchworm yellow.
Color the other letter inchworms red.

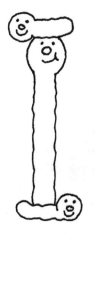

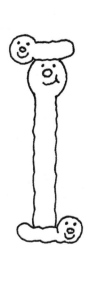

Inchworms are insects.
What other insects can you name?

SKILLS: Alphabet: letter names, recognize upper- and lowercase letters; **Writing:** color within the lines

Help Little find the **i** pictures.

Inchworms begins with the short **i** sound.

Color in the circle on the inchworms picture.

Name the other pictures.

Color in the circle on each picture that begins with the same sound as **inchworms**.

Draw an X on the pictures that do **not** begin like **inchworms**.

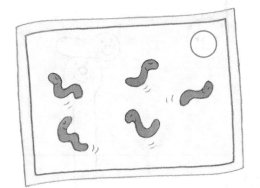

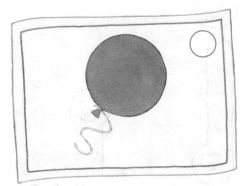

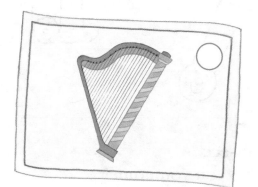

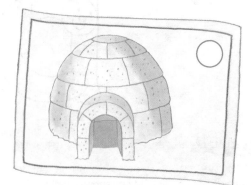

Phonics Note
The letter **i** stands for two sounds: short **i** as in insect, and long **i** as in island.

SKILLS: Phonemic Awareness: short i/i/; **Writing:** color within the lines, draw the letter X

Write i and I

Use your finger to trace the letters under the iguanas.
Start at the big dot.
Then use a crayon to trace and write the letters.

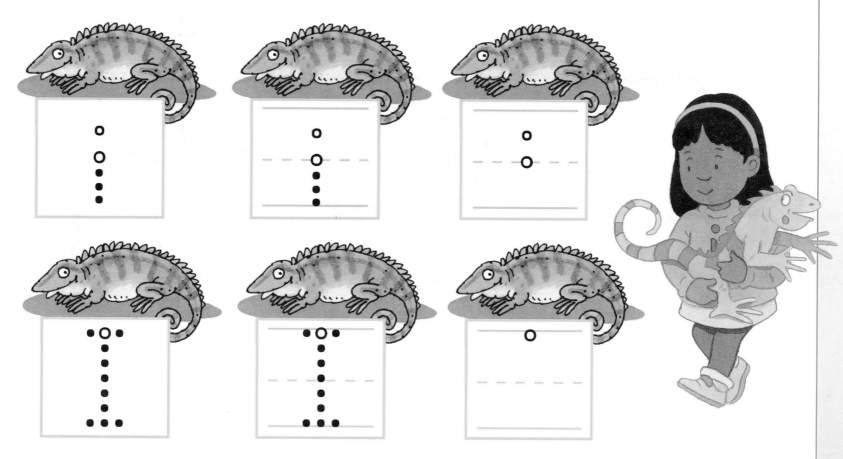

What kind of pet would you like to have?

SKILLS: Writing: finger-trace and write letters i, I

Name j and J

Name the letters on the jack-o'-lanterns.
Color each little **j** jack-o'-lantern red.
Color each big **J** jack-o'-lantern yellow.
Color the other letter jack-o'-lanterns green.

What do you like to dress up as on Halloween?

SKILLS: Alphabet: letter names, recognize upper- and lowercase letters; **Writing:** color within the lines

Hear the j Sound

Help Little  put the **j** words in the sound jar.
Jack-o'-lantern begins with the **j** sound.
Trace the line from the jack-o'-lantern to the sound jar.
Name the other pictures.
Draw a line from the pictures that begin with the first sound in **jack-o'-lantern** to the jar.

SKILLS: Phonemic Awareness: j/j/; Writing: draw lines top-to-bottom

Write j and J

Use your finger to trace the letters by the jellyfish.
Start at the big dot.
Then use a crayon to trace and write the letters.

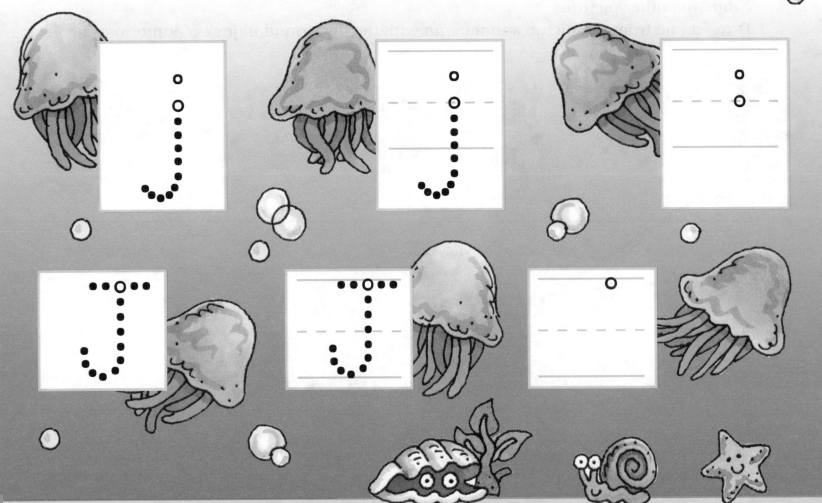

SKILLS: Writing: finger-trace and write letters j, J

Name k and K

Name the letters on the kittens.
Color each little **k** kitten yellow.
Draw red stripes on each big **K** kitten.
Color the other letter kittens blue.

K

F

k

k

e

K

What sound do kittens make?

SKILLS: Alphabet: letter names, recognize upper- and lowercase letters; **Writing:** color within the lines, draw stripes

Hear the k Sound

Little 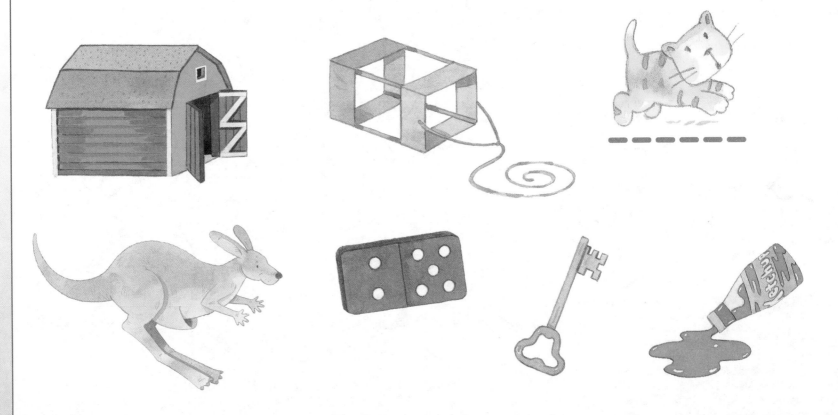 wants to play with things that begin with the **k** sound.
Kitten begins with the **k** sound.
Trace the line under the kitten.
Name the other pictures.
Draw a line under the pictures that begin with the first sound in **kitten**.

SKILLS: Phonemic Awareness: k/k/; **Writing:** learn to underline

Write k and K

Use your finger to trace the letters by the kangaroos.
Start at the big dot.
Then use a crayon to trace and write the letters.

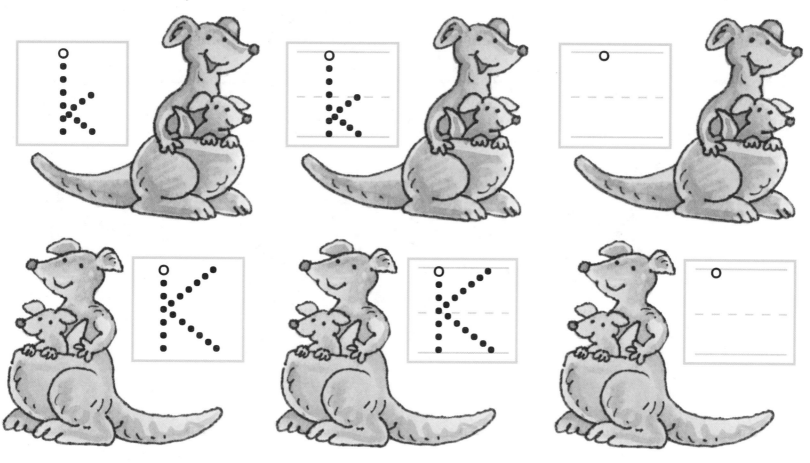

Can you hop like a kangaroo?

SKILLS: Writing: finger-trace and write letters k, K

Name l and L

Name the letters on the leaves.
Color each little **l** leaf green.
Color each big **L** leaf yellow.
Color the other letter leaves red.

Where do leaves come from?

Activity

A Little Like l Many lowercase letters have an **l** in them. Help your child find them! First, write all the lowercase letters on a piece of paper. Point to one letter at a time, and help your child finger-trace each letter. When it's a tall letter, point out that the first stroke is just like the letter **l**. Have your child identify them all.

SKILLS: Alphabet: letter names, recognize upper- and lowercase letters; **Writing:** color within the lines

Help Little 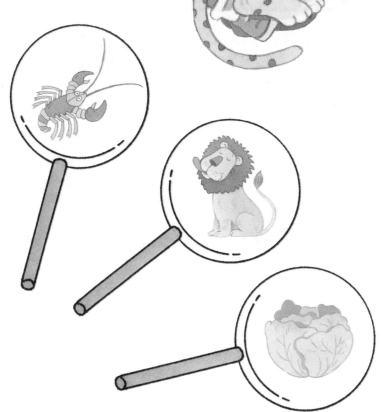 find the lollipops with **l** words on them.
Leopard begins with the **l** sound.
Name the pictures on the lollipops.
Draw a circle around the lollipops that begin with the first sound in **leopard**.
Draw an X on the lollipops that do **not** begin like **leopard**.

SKILLS: Phonemic Awareness: l/l/; Writing: draw circles and the letter X

Write l and L

Use your finger to trace the letters on the farm.
Start at the big dot.
Then use a crayon to trace and write the letters.

What other animals live on a farm?

SKILLS: Writing: finger-trace and write letters l, L

Name m and M

Name the letters on the pieces of cheese.
Color each little **m** cheese yellow.
Color each big **M** cheese red.
Color the other pieces of cheese blue.

What sound does a mouse make?

SKILLS: Alphabet: letter names, recognize upper- and lowercase letters; **Writing:** color within the lines

Help Little 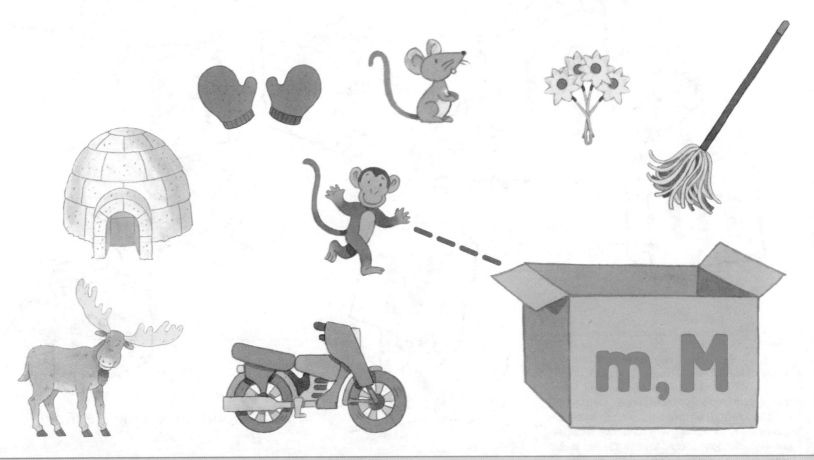 put the **m** words in the sound box.
Monkey begins with the **m** sound.
Trace the line from the monkey to the sound box.
Name the other pictures.
Draw a line from the pictures that begin with the first sound in **monkey** to the box.

SKILLS: Phonemic Awareness: m/m/; **Writing:** draw lines left-to-right and diagonal

Write m and M

Use your finger to trace the letter on each moose.
Start at the big dot.
Then use a crayon to trace and write the letters.

SKILLS: Writing: finger-trace and write letters **m, M**

Name the letters in the nets.
Color each little **n** net blue.
Color each big **N** net red.
Draw a box around the other letter nets.

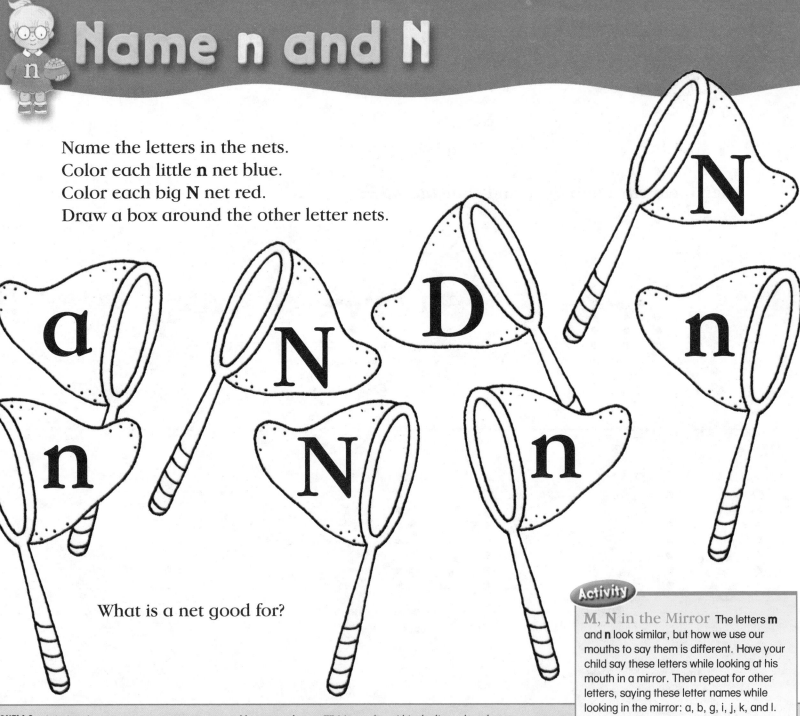

What is a net good for?

SKILLS: Alphabet: letter names, recognize upper- and lowercase letters; **Writing:** color within the lines, draw boxes

Hear the n Sound

Little  is going shopping. Help her buy things that begin with the **n** sound.
Net begins with the **n** sound.
Trace the circle around the net.
Name the other pictures.
Draw a circle around the pictures that begin with the first sound in **net**.
Then draw an X on the pictures that do **not** begin like **net**.

SKILLS: Phonemic Awareness: n/n/; **Writing:** draw circles and the letter X

Write n and N

Use your finger to trace the letters on the nuts.
Start at the big dot.
Then use a crayon to trace and write the letters.

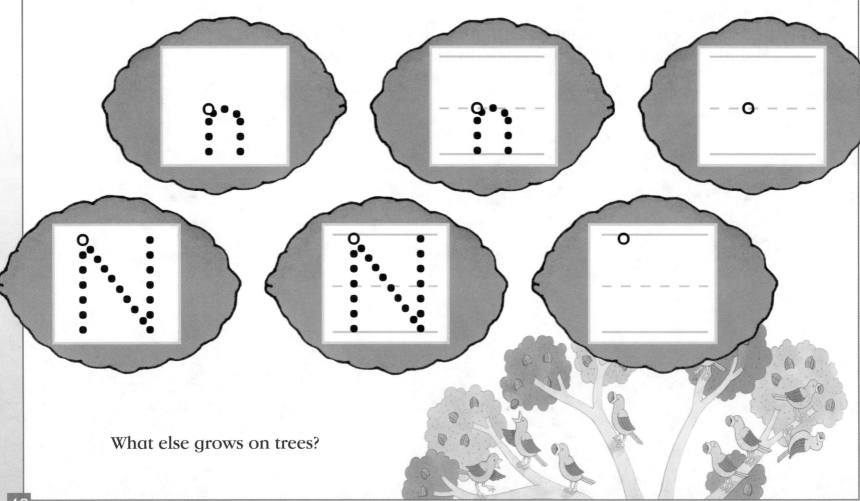

What else grows on trees?

SKILLS: Writing: finger-trace and write letters n, N

Name the letters on the octopus' tentacles.
Color each little **o** blue.
Color each big **O** red.
Color the other letters yellow.

Activity

Tic-Tac-Toe Reinforce the letters **O** and **X** by playing tic-tac-toe with your child. Then play using the letter **O** and the first letter of your child's name. Repeat with other letters.

Where does an octopus live?

49

SKILLS: Alphabet: letter names, recognize upper- and lowercase letters; **Writing:** color within the lines

Help Little **o** find the **o** animals.

Olive begins with the short **o** sound.

Name the pictures.

Draw a circle around the animals whose names begin with the first sound in **olive**.

Draw a line under the animals whose names do **not** begin like **olive**.

Phonics Note
The letter **o** stands for two sounds: short **o** as in **o**tter, and long **o** as in **o**cean.

SKILLS: Phonemic Awareness: short o/o/; **Writing:** draw circles, learn to underline

Write o and O

Use your finger to trace the letters on the oxen.
Start at the big dot.
Use your red crayon to trace and write each little **o**.
Then use your yellow crayon to trace and write each big **O**.

SKILLS: Writing: finger-trace and write letters o, O

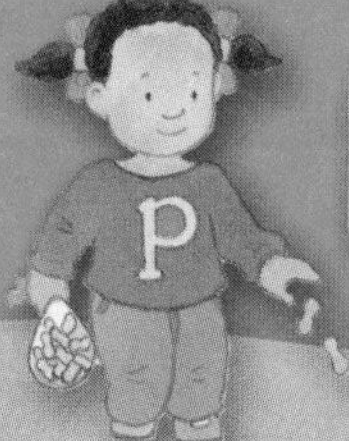

Name p and P

Name the letters on the pigs.
Color each little **p** pig red.
Color each big **P** pig yellow.
Draw an X on the other letter pigs.

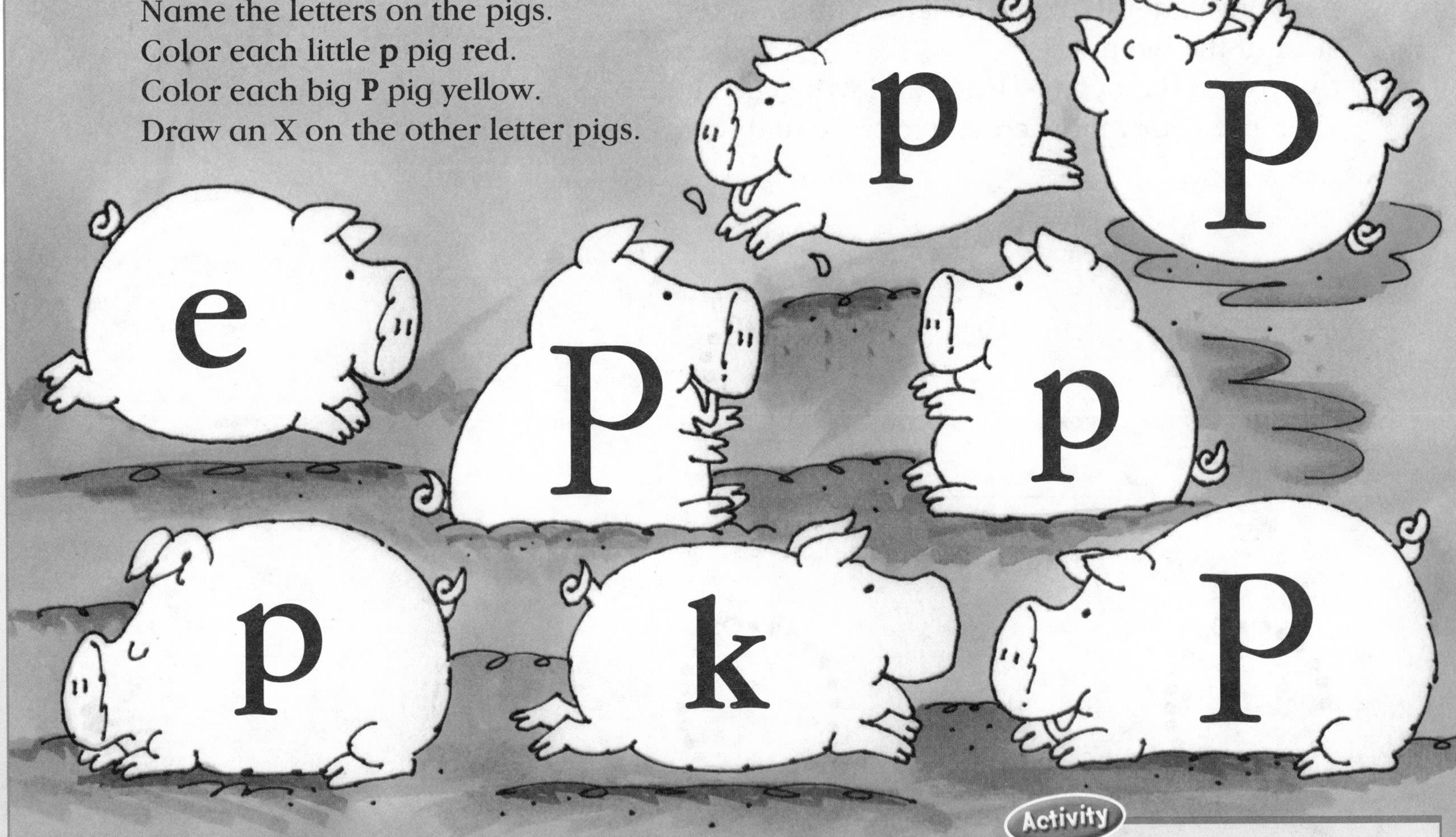

p

P

e

P

p

p

p

k

P

What is each pig doing?

SKILLS: Alphabet: letter names, recognize upper- and lowercase letters; **Writing:** color within the lines, draw the letter X

Hear the p Sound

Help Little 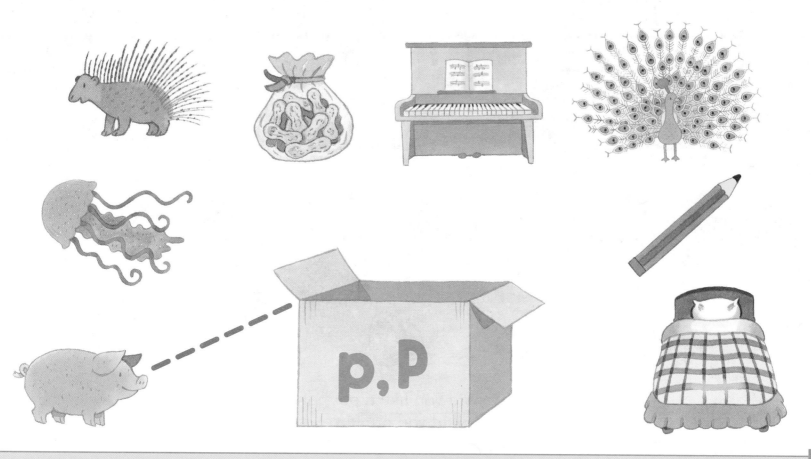 put the **p** words in the sound box.
Pig begins with the **p** sound.
Trace the line from the pig to the sound box.
Name the other pictures.
Draw a line from the pictures that begin with the first sound in **pig** to the box.

Write p and P

Use your finger to trace the letters next to the pandas.
Start at the big dot.
Then use a crayon to trace and write the letters.

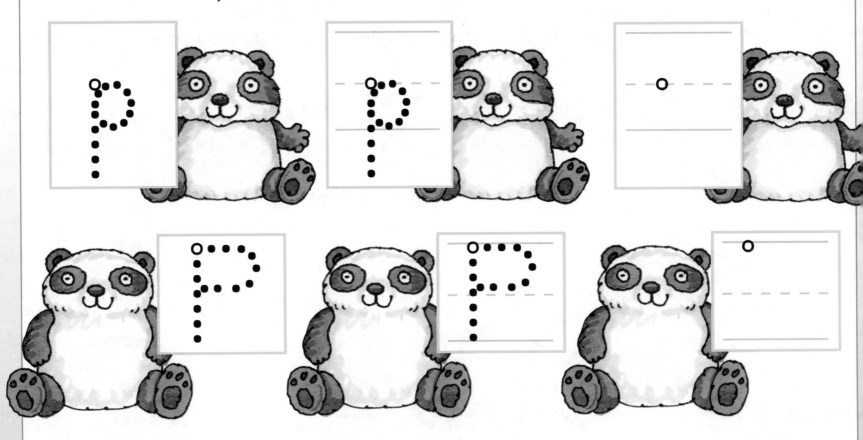

Would you like a pet panda?
What would you name your panda?

SKILLS: Writing: finger-trace and write letters p, P

Name q and Q

Can you name the letters on the quilts?
Color each little **q** red.
Color each big **Q** blue.
Color the other letters yellow.
Color the shapes on the quilts green.

Say the names of the shapes on the quilts.
What other shapes can you name?

Activity

4 Quarters Help your child understand the concept of quarters at snack time. Cut an apple into quarters. Tell your child that each quarter is one part of the whole. All four quarters make the whole apple. Count out the apple quarters: one quarter, two quarters, three quarters, a whole.

SKILLS: Alphabet: letter names, recognize upper- and lowercase letters; **Writing:** color within the lines

Write q and Q

Use your finger to trace the letters on the quarts of milk.
Start at the big dot.
Then use a crayon to trace and write the letters.

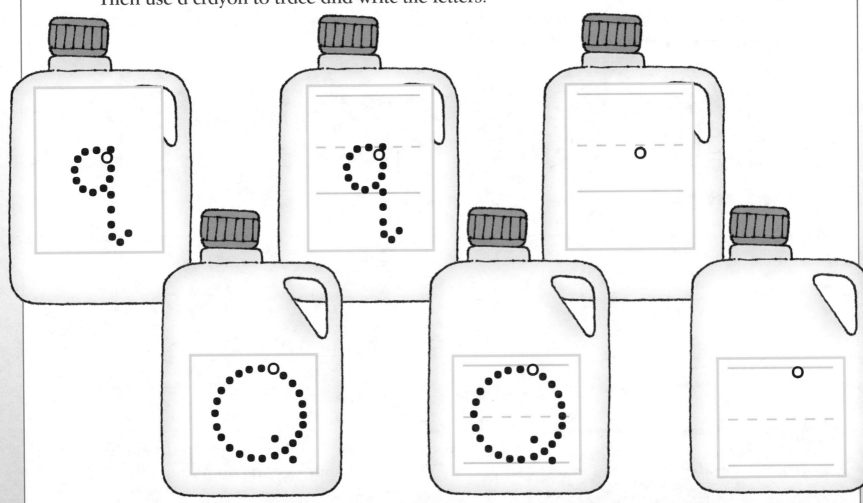

SKILLS: Writing: finger-trace and write letters q, Q

Name r and R

Name the letters on the rabbits.
Color each little **r** rabbit red.
Color each big **R** rabbit green.
Color the other letter rabbits blue.

Activity

That's Right! Tie a ribbon around your child's right wrist. Then walk around your house and have your child point to things that begin with the same sound as **right**. Each time your child correctly identifies an r-object, say, "Right!"

Can you hop like a rabbit?
What other animals hop?

SKILLS: Alphabet: letter names, recognize upper- and lowercase letters; **Writing:** color within the lines

Hear the r Sound

Little  is taking some friends for a ride in his rowboat.

Rock begins with the **r** sound.

Draw a circle around the friends that begin with the same sound as **rock**.

Draw an X on the friends that do **not** begin like **rock**.

SKILLS: Phonemic Awareness: r/r/; Writing: draw circles and the letter X

Write r and R

Use your finger to trace the letters on the resting rhinos.
Start at the big dot.
Then use a crayon to trace and write the letters.

Where do you like to rest?

SKILLS: Writing: finger-trace and write letters r, R

Name s and S

Name the letters on the socks.
Color each little **s** sock red.
Color each big **S** sock blue.
Draw an X on the socks with other letters on them.

 s

 S

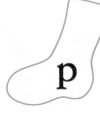 p

 B

 S

 s

 s

 S

Name the other clothing in the picture.
What are you wearing?

Activity

Silly Sentences Give your child's mouth a workout with silly *tongue twisters*. For the letter **s**, try these: Seven silver sails; Six seals sing silly songs; and Sally sold several sacks of sea salt. What other *tongue twisters* can you think of? Try other letters, too!

SKILLS: Alphabet: letter names, recognize upper- and lowercase letters; **Writing:** color within the lines, draw the letter X

Hear the s Sound

Help Little  put the **s** words in the sound box.
Sock begins with the **s** sound.
Trace the line from the sock to the sound box.
Name the other pictures.
Draw a line from the pictures that begin with
the first sound in **sock** to the sound box.

s, S

SKILLS: Phonemic Awareness: s/s/; Writing: draw lines from bottom-to-top and diagonal

Write s and S

Use your finger to trace the letters on the seals.
Start at the big dot.
Use your blue crayon to trace and write each little **s**.
Then use your green crayon to trace and write each big **S**.

Seals live in the ocean. What is another word for **ocean** that begins with the same sound as **seal**?

SKILLS: Writing: finger-trace and write letters s, S; Phonemic Awareness: s/s/

Name t and T

Name the letters on the turtles.
Draw a red circle around each little **t** turtle.
Draw a blue square around each big **T** turtle.
Draw an X on the turtles with other letters on them.

How do turtles move?
Can you crawl slowly like a turtle?

SKILLS: Alphabet: letter names, recognize upper- and lowercase letters; **Writing**: draw circles, squares, and the letter X

Hear the t Sound

Help Little  put the **t** words in his tent.
Turtle begins with the **t** sound.
Trace the line from the turtle to the tent.
Name the other pictures.
Draw a line from the pictures that begin with the same sound as **turtle** to the tent.
Draw an X on the pictures that do **not** begin like **turtle**.

SKILLS: Phonemic Awareness: t/t/; Writing: draw lines and the letter X

Write t and T

Use your finger to trace the letters on the tulips.
Start at the big dot.
Then use a crayon to trace and write the letters.

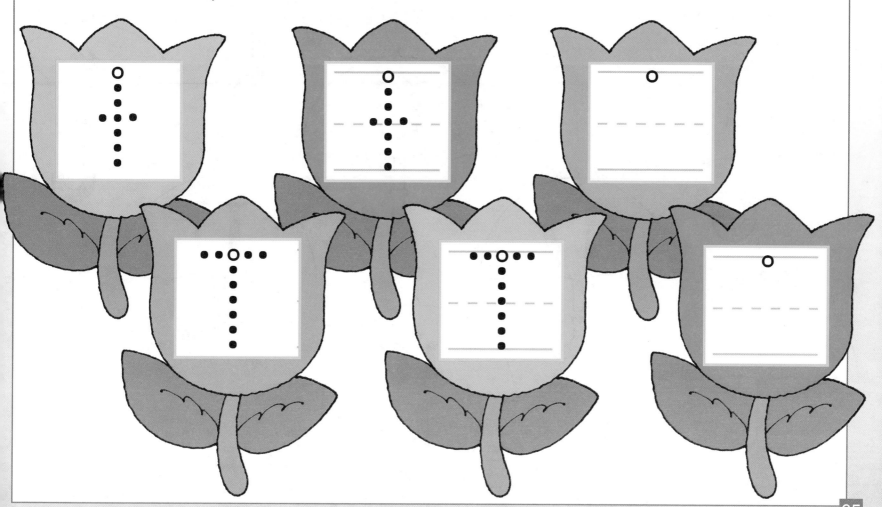

SKILLS: Writing: finger-trace and write letters t, T

Name the letters on the umbrellas.
Color each little **u** umbrella blue.
Color each big **U** umbrella red.
Draw green dots on the other letter umbrellas.

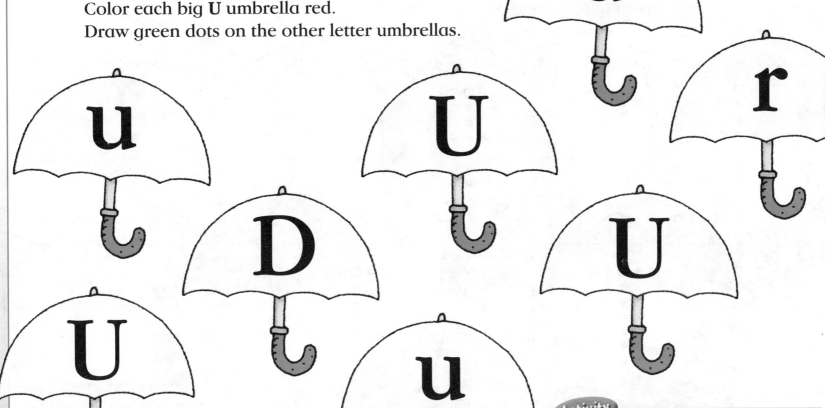

Activity

Simon Says Stand Up Play Simon Says
to reinforce the short **u** sound. Use Simon Says
commands such as: Stand **u**p, crawl **u**nder the
table, go **u**pstairs, and turn a cup **u**pside down.
After playing, ask your child to name the first sound
he or she hears in the words **up**, **under**, **upstairs**,
and **upside** down.

SKILLS: Alphabet: letter names, recognize upper- and lowercase letters; **Writing:** color within the lines, draw dots

Hear the Short u Sound

Follow the clues to find Little 's favorite places to play.
Umbrella begins with the short **u** sound.
Circle the places that begin with the first sound in **umbrella**.
She likes to climb **u**p the ladder.
She likes to hang **u**pside down on the jungle gym.
She likes to eat her lunch at the picnic table **u**nder the tree.

Phonics Note
The letter **u** stands for two sounds: short **u** as in **u**mbrella, and long **u** as in **u**nicorn.

What does Little **u** like to do that you like to do, too?

SKILLS: Phonemic Awareness: short u/u/; Writing: draw circles

Write u and U

Use your finger to trace the letters on the undershirts.
Start at the big dot.
Use your red crayon to trace and write each little **u**.
Then use your blue crayon to trace and write each big **U**.

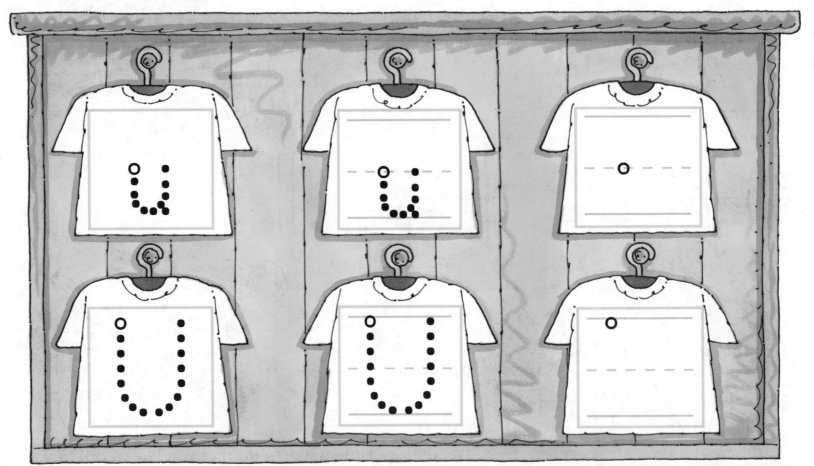

SKILLS: Writing: finger-trace and write letters u, U

Name the letters on the violins.
Color each little **v** violin red.
Color each big **V** violin yellow.
Color the other letter violins blue.

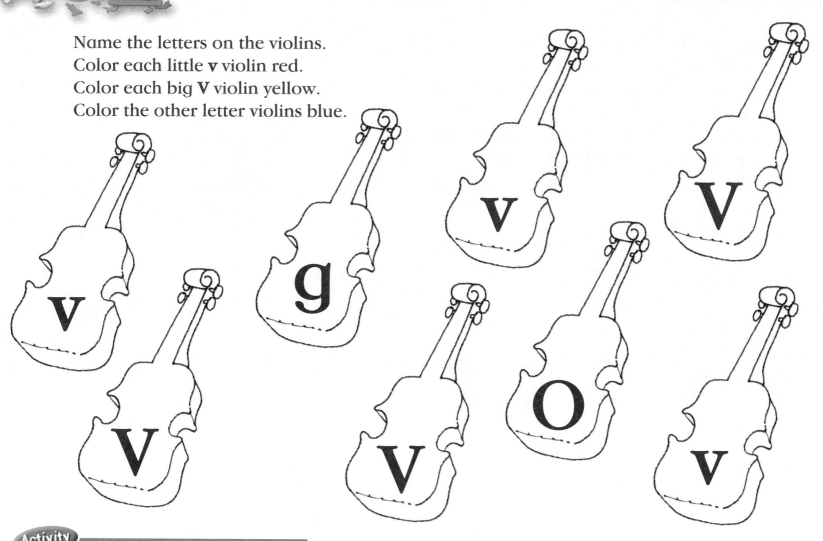

Activity

Very! What tastes very good? Ask your child to name other "very" things. For instance, something that is very funny, very surprising, very hot, very cold, and so on.

What other musical instruments can you name?

SKILLS: Alphabet: letter names, recognize upper- and lowercase letters; **Writing:** color within the lines

Hear the v Sound

Help Little  put the **v** words in the sound box.
Violin begins with the **v** sound.
Trace the line from the violin to the sound box.
Name the other pictures.
Draw a line from the pictures that begin with
the first sound in **violin** to the sound box.

v, V

SKILLS: Phonemic Awareness: v/v/; **Writing:** draw lines from right-to-left and diagonal

Write v and V

Use your finger to trace the letters by the vases.
Start at the big dot.
Use your yellow crayon to trace and write each little **v**.
Then use your green crayon to trace and write each big **V**.

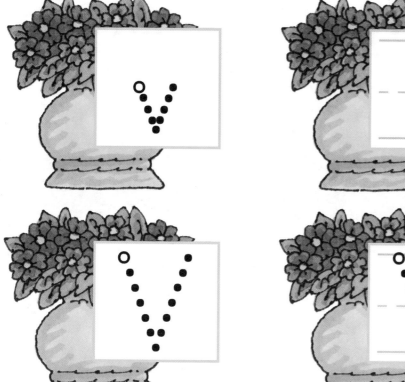

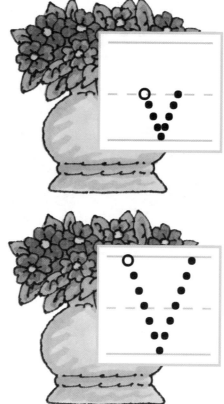

What flowers can you name?

SKILLS: Writing: finger-trace and write letters v, V

Name w and W

Name the letters in the water bubbles.
Color each little **w** bubble green.
Color each big **W** bubble blue.
Color the other letter bubbles yellow.

Where is the whale? What other
animals live in the water?

SKILLS: Alphabet: letter names, recognize upper- and lowercase letters; **Writing:** color within the lines

Hear the w Sound

Little  is walking in the woods.
She is looking for things that begin with the **w** sound.
Web begins with the **w** sound.
Circle the **7** things she sees whose names begin with
the same sound as **web**.

Where do you like to take a walk?
What do you see on your walk?

SKILLS: Phonemic Awareness: w/w/; Writing: draw circles

Write w and W

Use your finger to trace the letters by the windmills.
Start at the big dot.
Use your green crayon to trace and write each little **w**.
Then use your red crayon to trace and write each big **W**.

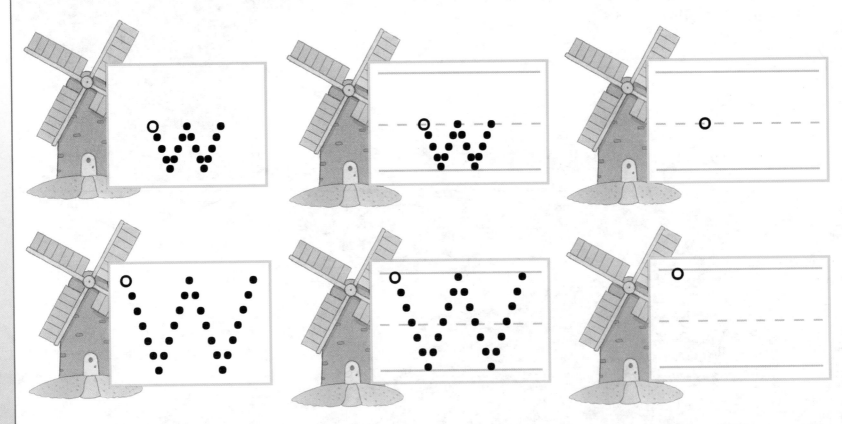

What does the wind do? How does the wind sound?

SKILLS: Writing: finger-trace and write letters w, W

Name the letters in the x-rays.
Color each little **x**, **y**, and **z** red.
Color each big **X**, **Y**, and **Z** blue.

Activity

X Marks the Spot **X**, **y**, and **z** are fun and easy to write in the sand or dirt. Next time your child's playing in the sandbox or you're taking a walk in the park, look for a stick your child can use to write letters in the dirt. Start with **x**, **y**, and **z**. Then add other straight-line letters, such as A, E, F, H, I, i, K, k, L, l, and so on.

SKILLS: Alphabet: letter names, recognize upper- and lowercase letters; **Writing:** color within the lines

75

Write x, X, y, Y, and z, Z

Use your finger to trace the letters.
Start at the big dot.
Then use a crayon to trace and write the letters.

SKILLS: Writing: finger-trace and write letters x, X, y, Y, z, Z

My First Steps Dictionary

A dictionary is a special book of words in ABC order.
Here are the letters and some pictures that begin with the letter sounds.
Can you name the letters and the pictures?
Listen for the first sound in each picture name.

a	apple	ant	g	guitar	goat
b	bear	ball	h	hat	horse
c	cat	car	i	insect	igloo
d	doll	dog	j	jack-o'-lantern	jellyfish
e	elf	elephant	k	kangaroo	kite
f	fork	frog	l	lion	lettuce

My First Steps Dictionary

m	monkey	mouse		t	turtle	tricycle
n	net	necklace		**u**	umbrella	unicorn
o	octopus	ostrich		**v**	violin	valentine
p	pig	piano		**w**	window	watch
q	quilt	queen		**x**	x-ray	xylophone
r	rabbit	rooster		**y**	yo-yo	yak
s	snail	sun		**z**	zebra	zipper

Learning Numbers

Have fun with Little One, Little Two, Little Three, and the other number kids from the storybooks. Learn their names, count and match their numbers to objects, and write their numbers and number words.

In this section, the pages for each number explore these concepts and skills:

- **Number Recognition**: As with the letter-sound correspondence, children need practice in recognizing and naming the numerical symbol.

- **Number Knowledge**: To demonstrate conceptual understanding, your child will circle, underline, and in other ways match numerals to the same number of objects.

- **Number Writing**: Your child will practice writing the numeral and tracing the number word.

Number 1

This is the number **1**.
This is the number word: **one**.

Draw a line from Little One to the number 1.
Color the 1 yellow.

2 4 1 3 5

You can write the number **1**.
Use your finger to trace the **1**.
Start at the big dot.
Use a crayon to trace and write the numbers.

Now you can write the number word **one**.
Use your finger to trace **one**.
Start each letter at the big dot.
Use a crayon to trace the word.

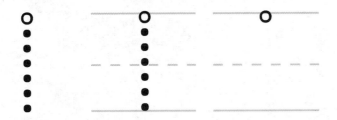

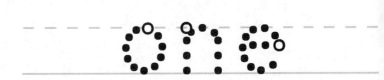

Let's Count!

Count the number of rooms in Little One's house.

Circle the number:

1   2   3   4   5

Little One wants to pull a friend in his wagon.
Can you draw **one** friend in his wagon?
What **1** friend will you draw?

Little One loves animals and wants **1** of each.
Draw a circle around each wagon with **one** animal in it.

Activity

Who's Number 1? How many number ones are there in your world? Have your child name singular things in his or her life, such as one mom, one brother, one cat, and so on.

SKILLS: Math: number names, number recognition, counting; Writing: draw lines and circles, color within the lines, finger-trace and write numeral 1, trace number word one

Number 2

This is the number **2**.
This is the number word: **two**.

Draw a line from Little Two to the number 2.
Color the 2 red.

5 2

You can write the number **2**.
Use your finger to trace the **2**.
Start at the big dot.
Use a crayon to trace and write the numbers.

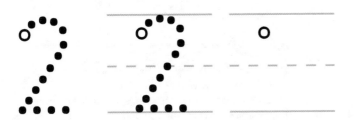

Now you can write the number word **two**.
Use your finger to trace **two**.
Start each letter at the big dot.
Use a crayon to trace the word.

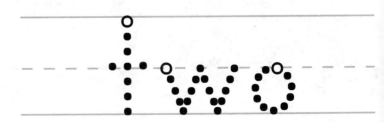

Let's Count!

Count the number of rooms in Little Two's house.

Circle the number:

1 2 3 4 5

Little Two puts on her sneakers to go play outside.
Think of **two** things you like to wear when you play outside.
Then draw the **2** things to wear in the box. Tell about your picture.

Little Two went for a walk.
She found **2** butterflies, **2** lambs, **2** chicks, and **2** frogs.
Draw a line under each group of **two**.

Activity

Pairs It's time to practice pairs! Go on a pairs hunt with your child. Find things that come in pairs, starting with parts of your child's body.

Number 3

This is the number **3**.
This is the number word: **three**.

Draw a line from Little Three to the number 3.
Color the 3 blue.

1 5 4 2 3

You can write the number **3**.
Use your finger to trace the **3**.
Start at the big dot.
Use a crayon to trace and write the numbers.

Now you can write the number word **three**.
Use your finger to trace **three**.
Start each letter at the big dot.
Use a crayon to trace the word.

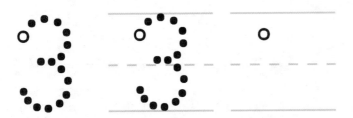

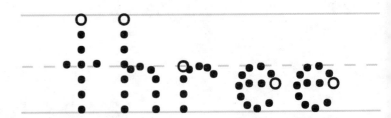

Let's Count!

Count the number of rooms
in Little Three's house.

Circle the number:

1   2   3   4   5

Little Three likes to help her friends.
One day, she helps **3** pigs, **3** bears, and **3** goats.
Draw a circle around each group of **three**.

Happy Birthday, Little Three!
She loves birthday cake!
Help decorate this birthday cake.
Draw **three** candles on it.
Use **3** different colors.
Then decorate the cake!

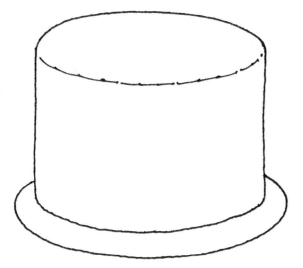

Activity

Once Upon a Time   **Three** is a magical number often used in folk and fairy tales. When you share these types of stories with your child, encourage him or her to count the three characters and/or objects when they appear.

Number 4

This is the number **4**.
This is the number word: **four**.

Draw a line from Little Four to the number 4.
Color the 4 green.

2   5   3   4   1

You can write the number **4**.
Use your finger to trace the 4.
Start at the big dot.
Use a crayon to trace and write the numbers.

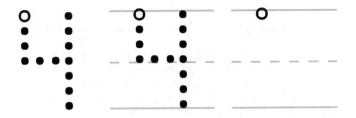

Now you can write the number word **four**.
Use your finger to trace **four**.
Start each letter at the big dot.
Use a crayon to trace the word.

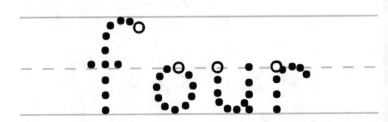

Let's Count!

Count the number of rooms in Little Four's house.

Circle the number:

1   2   3   4   5

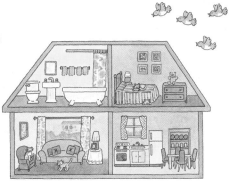

Little Four loves ice cream cones. Do you like ice cream? Draw **four** scoops of ice cream on this cone. Color the **4** scoops and name the flavors.

Little Four went to the zoo. He saw **4** of each animal. Draw a box around each group of **four** animals.

Number 5

This is the number **5**.
This is the number word: **five**.

Draw a line from Little Five to the number 5.
Color the 5 yellow.

 5 1 2 3 4

You can write the number **5**.
Use your finger to trace the **5**.
Start at the big dot.
Use a crayon to trace and write the numbers.

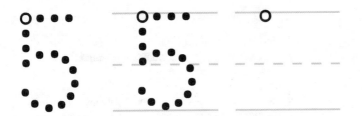

Now you can write the number word **five**.
Use your finger to trace **five**.
Start each letter at the big dot.
Use a crayon to trace the word.

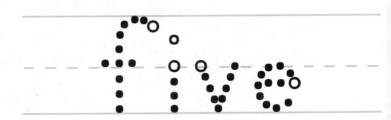

Let's Count!

Count the number of rooms in Little Five's house.

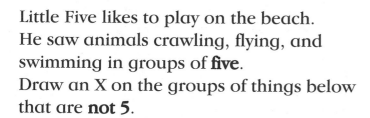

Circle the number:

1   2   3   4   5

Little Five likes to play on the beach.
He saw animals crawling, flying, and swimming in groups of **five**.
Draw an X on the groups of things below that are **not 5**.

Little Five wants to go fishing, but there are no fish in the pond!
Draw **5** fish for him to catch.
Tell about the **five** fish you drew.

Activity

I Have Five! **Five** is not just a prime number—it is also an organic number. Help your child count body fives: five fingers on each hand, five toes on each foot. Then have your child clap, jump, and hop five times.

Let's count the numbers from 1 to 5.
Draw a line from each number friend to his or her number below.

Color the numbers.
Then draw a line from the number to the matching number word.

2 4 1 5 3

five two one three four

Circus wheels go 'round and 'round.
How many wheels do you see?
Write the number of wheels each item has next to it.

What number comes next? Write the missing numbers.

I, _____

I, 2, _____

2, 3, _____

3, 4, _____

SKILLS: Math: number names, number recognition, number sequence, counting; **Writing:** draw lines, color within the lines, write numerals **1 to 5**

Number 6

This is the number **6**.
This is the number word: **six**.

Draw a line from Little Six to the number 6.
Color the 6 red.

5 7 8 6 4

You can write the number **6**.
Use your finger to trace the 6.
Start at the big dot.
Use a crayon to trace and write the numbers.

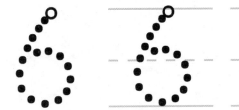

Now you can write the number word **six**.
Use your finger to trace **six**.
Start each letter at the big dot.
Use a crayon to trace the word.

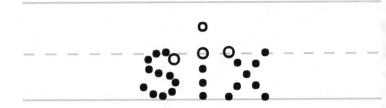

Let's Count!

Count the number of rooms in Little Six's house.

Circle the number:

6   7   8   9   10

Little Six found a nest!
What do you think she saw inside?
Draw **6** things in this nest.
What **six** things did you draw?

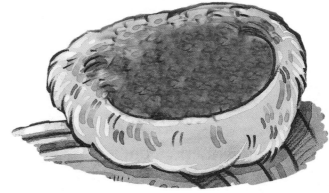

Little Six went out to explore the woods.
She saw lots of trees—with lots of animals in them!
Circle each tree that has **6** animals. Name the animals.

 Activity

Let's Make 6 Practice counting to **six** by placing six items in a row. Have your child count them. Then give three of the items to your child. Say, "You have 3. I have 3. How many do we have all together?" Repeat for 4 and 2, 2 and 4, 5 and 1, and 1 and 5.

SKILLS: Math: number names, number recognition, counting; **Writing:** draw lines and circles, color within the lines, finger-trace and write numeral 6, trace number word **six**

Number 7

This is the number 7.
This is the number word: **seven**.

Draw a line from Little Seven to the number 7.
Color the 7 blue.

 9 7 5    8 6

You can write the number 7.
Use your finger to trace the 7.
Start at the big dot.
Use a crayon to trace and write the numbers.

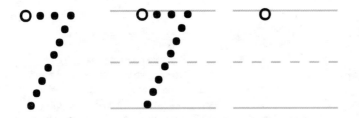

Now you can write the number word **seven**.
Use your finger to trace **seven**.
Start each letter at the big dot.
Use a crayon to trace the word.

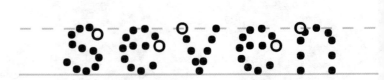

Let's Count!

Count the number of rooms in Little Seven's house.

Circle the number:

6   7   8   9   10

Little Seven walked to the pond.
What did Little Seven find?
Draw a line under each group of **7**.

Little Seven likes to play in the sandbox.
Draw **7** things to play with in this sandbox.
What can Little Seven do with the **seven** things you drew?

Activity

Seven Remembering is an important skill. Revisit the book and point out all the different things Little Seven does: he walks, kneels, claps, sits, jumps, picks up pennies, and buys lollipops. Then help your child recall and count **seven** different things he did today. Praise his (and your own!) memory.

SKILLS: Math: number names, number recognition, counting; **Writing:** draw lines and circles, color within the lines, finger-trace and write numeral 7, trace number word **seven**

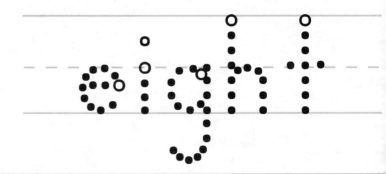

This is the number **8**.
This is the number word: **eight**.

Draw a line from Little Eight to the number 8.
Color the 8 green.

You can write the number **8**.
Use your finger to trace the **8**.
Start at the big dot.
Use a crayon to trace and write the numbers.

 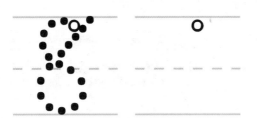

Now you can write the number word **eight**.
Use your finger to trace **eight**.
Start each letter at the big dot.
Use a crayon to trace the word.

Let's Count!

Count the number of rooms in Little Eight's house.

Circle the number:

6   7   8   9   10

Little Eight likes having tea parties—especially when there are yummy treats!
Draw **8** things you like to eat.
Tell about your picture.

Little Eight visited a farm.
She counted groups of **eight** things on the farm.
Circle the groups of **8**.

SKILLS: Math: number names, number recognition, counting; **Writing:** draw lines and circles, color within the lines, finger-trace and write numeral 8, trace number word **eight**

Number 9

This is the number **9**.
This is the number word: **nine**.

Draw a line from Little Nine to the number 9.
Color the 9 yellow.

You can write the number **9**.
Use your finger to trace the **9**.
Start at the big dot.
Use a crayon to trace and write the numbers.

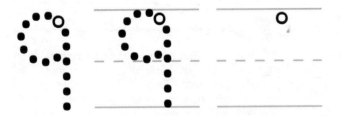

Now you can write the number word **nine**.
Use your finger to trace **nine**.
Start each letter at the big dot.
Use a crayon to trace the word.

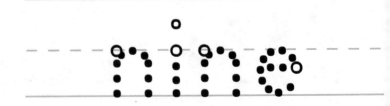

Let's Count!

Count the number of rooms in Little Nine's house.

Circle the number:

6 7 8 9 10

Little Nine has a shirt with nine dots on it.
Draw **9** dots on the shirt.
What colors are your dots?

Little Nine loves toys—especially playing with them!
Circle the sets of **9** toys.

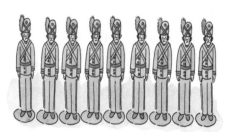

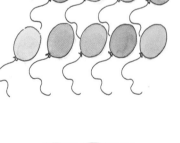

Activity

Tic-Tac-**Nine** Games like Tic-Tac-Toe and Sudoku are played on 9-box grids. Practice counting to **nine** by drawing a large 3x3 grid on a piece of paper. Have your child put a raisin or cereal o in each space and count the number of snacks. Then remove the snacks and use them to play Tic-Tac-Toe.

SKILLS: Math: number names, number recognition, counting; **Writing:** draw lines and circles, color within the lines, finger-trace and write numeral 9, trace number word **nine**

Number 10

This is the number **10**.
This is the number word: **ten**.

Draw a line from Little Ten to the number 10.
Color the 10 red.

You can write the number **10**.
Use your finger to trace the **10**.
Start at the big dot.
Use a crayon to trace and write the numbers.

Now you can write the number word **ten**.
Use your finger to trace **ten**.
Start each letter at the big dot.
Use a crayon to trace the word.

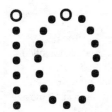 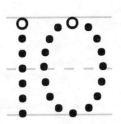 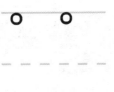

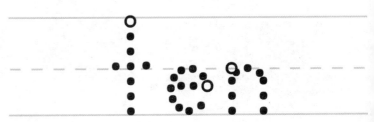

Let's Count!

Count the number of rooms
in Little Ten's house.

Circle the number:

6   7   8   9   10

Little Ten picks flowers for
her **ten** dolls.
Draw **10** pretty flowers.
What color are your flowers?

Little Ten had a tea party for her **ten** dolls.
She made a hat and a cupcake for each doll.
Count each group of dolls, hats, and cupcakes.
Draw an X on the groups that are **not 10**.

Numbers 6, 7, 8, 9, 10

Let's count the numbers from 6 to 10.
Draw a line from each number friend to his or her number below.

Color the numbers.
Then draw a line from the number to the matching number word.

ten seven nine six eight

Let's fly kites! How many bows are on the tail of each kite?
Count the number of bows on each kite.
Then trace the number on the kite. Color them, too!

What number comes before? Write the missing numbers.

_____ , 7, 8   _____ , 8, 9   _____ , 9, 10   _____ , 10

SKILLS: Math: number names, number recognition, number sequence, counting; Writing: draw lines, color within the lines, write numerals 6 to 10

Numbers 1 to 10

All of the numbers from 1 to 10 are hiding in the backyard.
Can you find them all?
Circle each number as you find it.

SKILLS: Math: number recognition; **Writing:** draw circles

Learning First Words

Little **a**, Little **z**, and all their friends invite you to play with words that begin with their letters!

The first word pages in this section explore these skills and concepts:

- **Phonics**: The words and pictures on these pages will give your child practice in sound-spelling connections by matching pictures to words. Encourage your child to find the words in the storybooks and on these pages.

- **Writing**: Tracing and writing the first letter for each picture label.

- **Your Name**: After reading words from the storybooks, help your child write and read a very important word—your child's name!

Come play a picture matching game with Little **a** and Little **b**!
Say the name of each picture.
Draw a line from each picture to the picture name.
Then read the words again.

| alligator | apple | ant | bear | banana | ball |

Activity

A Clap or Two or Three Introduce the concept of word parts (syllables) with a clapping game. Say a word and clap once for each syllable. For example, **ant** is one clap, **apple** is two. Clap the a- and b-words on this page. Then clap the names of family members and friends.

SKILLS: Phonics: short a/a, b/b/; **Writing:** draw lines bottom-to-top

My Words Starting With c and d

Can you write Little **c** and Little **d**'s letters?
First say the name of each picture.
Write the first letter of the picture name on the lines.
Then read all the words.

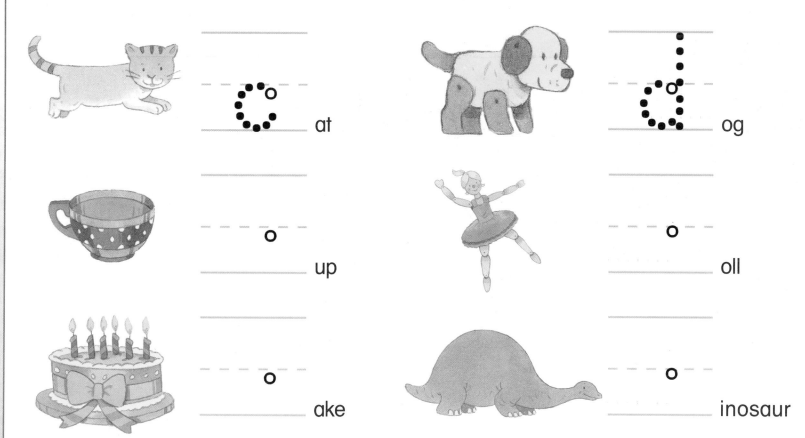

c at

d og

up

oll

ake

inosaur

SKILLS: Phonics: hard c/k/, d/d/; Writing: trace and write letters c, d

My Words Starting With e and f

Help Little **e** and Little **f** find the pictures that do not belong.
Name the letter and the pictures in each row.
Draw an X on the picture that does not begin with the same letter.
Next write the first letter in each picture name on the lines.
Then read all the words.

gg　　　　　lf　　　　　og　　　　　lephant

ish　　　　　ear　　　　　rog　　　　　irefighter

SKILLS: Phonics: short e/e/, f /f/; **Writing:** draw the letter X, trace and write letters **e**, **f**

My Words Starting With g and h

It's time to play Little **g** and Little **h**'s picture naming game!
Touch each picture and say its name.
Draw a circle around each animal.
Draw a line under each musical instrument.

Activity

Long and Tall With your child, write the letters **g** and **h** on a line. Point out how the **g** goes below the line. It is a long letter. Then point to the tall **h**. Have your child find another tall letter on this page. Then write family names on a piece of paper. Have your child trace the tall letters in one color and the long letters in another.

109

SKILLS: Phonics: hard g/g/, h/h/; **Writing:** draw circles, learn to underline

My Words Starting With i and j

Come play a picture matching game with Little **i** and Little **j**!
Say the name of each picture.
Draw a line from each picture to the picture name.
Then read the words again.

| ink | igloo | inchworm | jellyfish | jacket | jack-o'-lantern |

Activity

$1 + 1 = 1$ Use eyeglasses to explain **compound words**—big words made of two small words. The meaning of small words can be clues to the meaning of the compound (glasses for your eyes). Talk about the small words in the compound words on this page. Then hunt for compound words at home (bedroom, tablecloth, etc.).

SKILLS: Phonics: short i/i/, j/j/; **Writing:** draw lines bottom-to-top

Can you write Little **k** and Little **l**'s letters?
First say the name of each picture.
Write the first letter of the picture name on the lines.
Then read all the words.

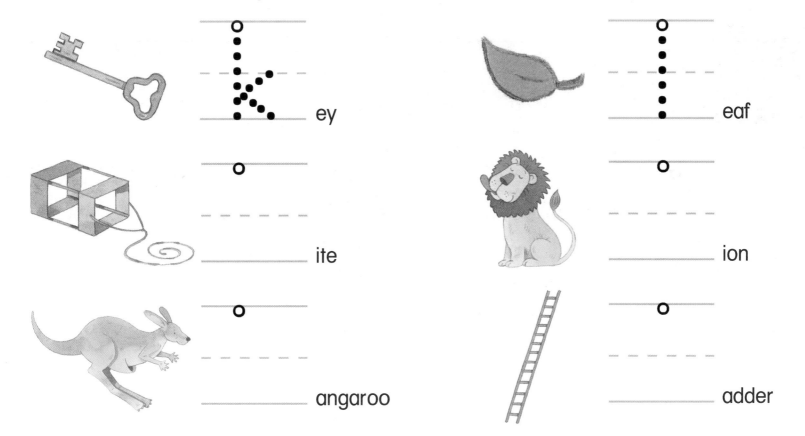

k _____ ey

_____ ite

_____ angaroo

l _____ eaf

_____ ion

_____ adder

SKILLS: Phonics: k/k/, l/l/; **Writing:** trace and write letters k, l

Help Little **m** and Little **n** find the pictures that do not belong.
Name the letter and the pictures in each row.
Draw an X on the picture that does not begin with the same letter.
Next write the first letter in each picture name on the lines.
Then read all the words.

m

oon ook op ouse

n

et ut oat eedle

SKILLS: Phonics: m/m/, n/n/; **Writing:** draw the letter X, trace and write letters **m**, **n**

It's time to play Little **o** and Little **p**'s picture naming game!
Touch each picture and say its name.
Draw a circle around each food.
Draw a line under each animal.

Activity

Letters in the Sand For extra letter-writing practice, fill a shallow pan with sand or salt. Then name a letter and have your child finger-write it in the sand. You can also use riddles, for example, "What letter stands for the first sound in a bird's home?"

SKILLS: Phonics: short o/o/, p/p/; **Writing:** draw circles, learn to underline

Come play a picture matching game with Little **q** and Little **r**!
Say the name of each picture.
Draw a line from each picture to the picture name.
Then read the words again.

queen

quilt

quail

rooster

ring

rabbit

Activity

Quiet as a ... Ask your child to name something that he or she does quietly. Then name activities that can be loud. Explain that the words **quiet** and **loud** have opposite meanings. Talk (quietly) about other opposites, such as up-down, in-out, top-bottom, day-night, happy-sad, and so on.

SKILLS: Phonics: q/kw/, r/r/; **Writing:** draw lines right-to-left

My Words Starting With s and t

Can you write Little **s** and Little **t**'s letters?
First say the name of each picture.
Write the first letter of the picture name on the lines.
Then read all the words.

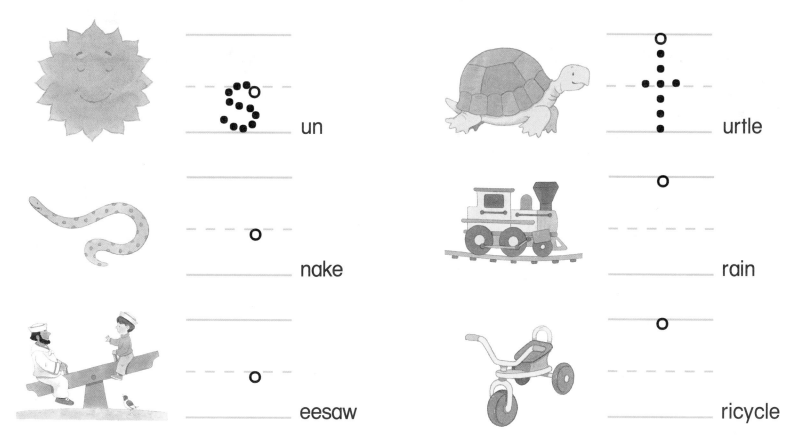

s un

t urtle

___ nake

___ rain

___ eesaw

___ ricycle

SKILLS: Phonics: s/s/, t/t/; Writing: trace and write letters s, t

My Words Starting With u and v

Help Little **u** and Little **v** find the pictures that do not belong.
Name the letter and the pictures in each row.
Draw an X on the picture that does not begin with the same letter.
Next write the first letter in each picture name on the lines.
Then read all the words.

u

 mbrella    nicorn   p   aw

v

 acuum   iolin   ey   ine

SKILLS: Phonics: u/u/, v/v/; Writing: draw the letter X, trace and write letters u, v

My Words Starting With w and x

It's time to play Little **w** and Little **x**'s picture naming game!
Touch each picture and say its name.
Draw a circle around the things that are round.
Draw a line under the things that have 4 sides.

SKILLS: Phonics: w/w/, x/x/; Writing: draw circles, learn to underline

My Words Starting With y and z

Come play a picture matching game with Little **y** and Little **z**!
Say the name of each picture.
Draw a line from each picture to the picture name.
Then read the words again.

| yak | yarn | yo-yo | zoo | zebra | zipper |

SKILLS: Phonics: y/y/, z/z/; **Writing:** draw lines top-to-bottom

Your Name

All the children in the a-to-z storybooks wear a letter.
What letter will you wear?
Write the first letter in your name on the shirt.

What letters are in your name?
Touch each of your storybook friends who are in your name.

Now write your name to finish the sentence.

My name is _____.

SKILLS: **Alphabet**: identify first initial; **Writing**: write your name

Good for You!

You finished the workbook! Good job!
Now write your name on the line.
Then read your diploma.
Next say the letters of the alphabet and count from 1 to 10.
Good for you!

I know the letters from A to Z.

I am very proud of me!

And the numbers 1 to 10,

I can count again and again!

Your Child's Name